The Beach

Building Longer Sequences

by Lynn Maslen Kertell
pictures by Sue Hendra and John R. Maslen

Scholastic Inc.
New York • Toronto • London • Auckland • Sydney • Mexico City • New Delhi • Hong Kong • Buenos Aires

"Who wants to go to the beach?"
asked Sally.

2

"I do, I do, I do!"
shouted her friends.

"What is the first thing we need to do?"
asked Sally.

"Pack snacks," said Tanner.
"Remember towels," said Dot.

"We're packed!" said Sally.
"What's next?"

"Put on sunscreen and swimsuits," said Seth.

"I'm done," said Sally. "Now what
is next?" "Hop in the car," said Mat.
"Let's go!"

They buckled up and
drove to the beach.

"We know what we want to
do next!" shouted Tanner.

"Jump in the water!" said Sally.

Thank goodness they had nothing else to do but play all day in the sparkling surf.